DIG FOR CLAMS

written by Paula Oliver
illustrated by Diane Blasius

McGraw-Hill
School Division

New York   Farmington

Jill and I have lots of fun.
We dig for clams in the
sand.

We feel the crisp wind and the soft black mud. Globs of mud stick to us. But we do not care!

Look at that! A crab rushes
past and a fat glob of mud
almost hits him.

We look for big, old clams.
We brush them and put
them in a bucket.

We put any small clams back
in the mud. Small clams are
new and still have to grow.

The clams go in the pickup
truck.

At home, we wash the clams.
Dad drops them in a hot
pot. We jump up and down.
Clams are the best!